West End

Show Hits

Wise Publications
part of The Music Sales Group
London/New York/Paris/Sydney/Copenhagen/Berlin/Madrid/Tokyo

Published by
Wise Publications
8/9 Frith Street, London W1D 3JB, UK

Exclusive Distributors
Music Sales Limited
Distribution Centre, Newmarket Road,
Bury St Edmunds, Suffolk IP33 3YB, UK
Music Sales Pty Limited
120 Rothschild Avenue,
Rosebery, NSW 2018,
Australia

Order No. AM982872
ISBN 1-84609-057-1
This book © Copyright 2005
Wise Publications,
a division of Music Sales Limited

New music arrangements by Jack Long,
processed Paul Ewers by Music Design
Compiled by Nick Crispin
Cover design by Esterson Associates
Printed in Great Britain

Your Guarantee of Quality
As publishers, we strive to produce every book to the highest commercial standards.
This book has been carefully designed to minimise awkward page turns and to make playing from it a real pleasure.
Particular care has been given to specifying acid-free, neutral-sized paper made from pulps which have not been elemental chlorine bleached. This pulp is from farmed sustainable forests and was produced with special regard for the environment.
Throughout, the printing and binding have been planned to ensure a sturdy, attractive publication which should give years of enjoyment. If your copy fails to meet our high standards, please inform us and we will gladly replace it.

www.musicsales.com

Also Available
West End Hit Songs
A great collection of 29 favourite stage hits.
Order No. AM91554

West End Love Songs
Thirty-four of the best romantic songs from London's musicals.
Order No. AM91665

Cabaret

(from 'Cabaret')

Words by Fred Ebb
Music by John Kander

Cabaret

(from 'Cabaret')

Words by Fred Ebb
Music by John Kander

Suitcase In Another Hall

(from 'Evita')

Music by Andrew Lloyd Webber
Lyrics by Tim Rice

MISTRESS

1. I don't ex - pect my love af - fairs___ to
(Verses 2 & 3 see block lyric)

last for long, nev - er fool my - self that my dreams___ will come true.

go - ing   to?___   go - ing   to?___

Verse 2:
Time and time again I've said that I don't care,
That I'm immune to gloom, that I'm hard through and through.
But every time it matters all my words desert me,
So anyone can hurt me – and they do.

So what happens now?…

Verse 3:
Call in three months' time and I'll be fine I know,
Well maybe not that fine, but I'll survive anyhow.
I won't recall the names and places of each sad occasion,
But that's no consolation, here and now.

So what happens now?…

Anything But Lonely

(from 'Aspects Of Love')

Music by Andrew Lloyd Webber
Lyrics by Don Black & Charles Hart

A - ny-thing but lone - ly, a - ny-thing but emp-ty rooms.

There's so much in life to share— what's the sense when no - one else is

there? What's the sense when

no one else is there? _____

Bangkok
(from 'Chess')

Words & Music by Benny Andersson, Tim Rice & Bjorn Ulvaeus

One Night In Bangkok
(from 'Chess')

Words & Music by Benny Andersson, Tim Rice & Bjorn Ulvaeus

Close Every Door

(from 'Joseph And The Amazing Technicolor® Dreamcoat')

Music by Andrew Lloyd Webber
Lyrics by Tim Rice

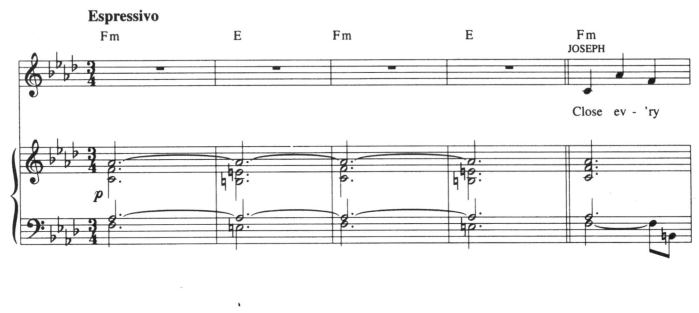

Children of Israel are nev-er a-lone for I

know I shall find my own peace 'of mind, for

I have been pro-mised a land of my own.

(Choir) Close ev-'ry door to me, hide all the world from me,

ask will I live or die, but I know the ans-wers lie far from this world.

Slower

Close ev-'ry door to me, keep those I love from me

child-ren of Is-rael are nev-er a-lone, for we know we shall find our—

own peace of mind, for we have been pro-mised, a land— of our own.

optional

rall.

37

Company

(from 'Company')

Words & Music by Stephen Sondheim

Late nights, quick bites, par-ty games,
deep talks, long walks, te-le-phone calls,
thoughts shared, souls bared, pri-vate names,
all those pho-tos up on the walls,
"With love," with love fill-ing the days,

Chim Chim Cher-ee

(from 'Mary Poppins')

Words & Music by Richard M. Sherman & Robert B. Sherman

CHORUS

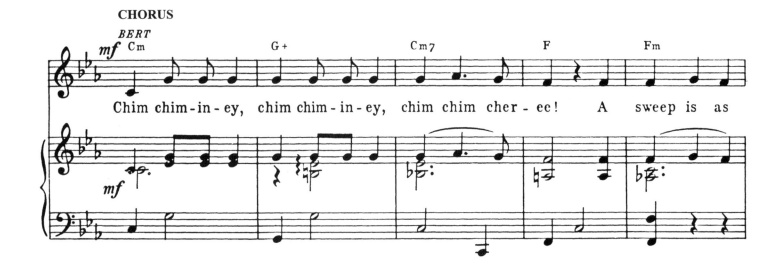

Chim chim-in-ey, chim chim-in-ey, chim chim cher-ee! A sweep is as

luck-y, as luck-y can be. Chim chim-in-ey, chim chim-in-ey,

chim chim cher-oo! Good luck will rub off when I shakes 'ands with
you, Or blow me a kiss and that's luck-y, too.

VERSE

Now, as the lad-der of
I choose me bris-tles with

life 'as been strung, You may think a sweep's on the bot-tom-most
pride, yes, I do: A broom for the shaft and a brush for the

43

rung. Though I spends me time in the ash-es and smoke, In
flue. Though I'm cov-ered with soot from me 'ead to me toes, A

this 'ole wide world there's no 'ap-pi-er bloke.
sweep knows 'e's wel-come wher-ev-er 'e goes.

Up where the smoke is all bill-ered and curled, 'Tween pave-ment and

stars, is the chim-ney sweep world. When there's 'ard-ly no day nor

No - where is there a more 'ap - pi - er crew Than

them wot sings, "Chim chim cher - ee, chim cher - oo!"

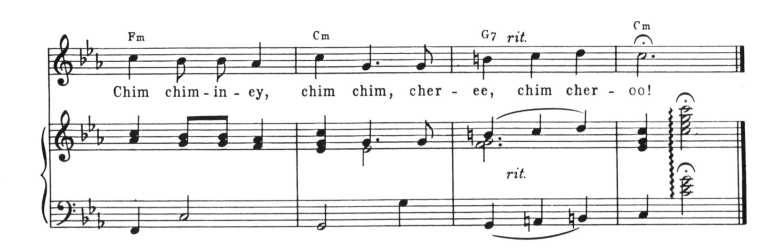

Chim chim - in - ey, chim chim, cher - ee, chim cher - oo!

Diamonds Are A Girl's Best Friend

(from 'Gentlemen Prefer Blondes')

Words by Leo Robin
Music by Jule Styne

Bright swing

kiss on the hand may be quite con - ti - nen - tal, but
may come a time when a lass needs a law - yer, but

dia - monds are a girl's best friend.
dia - monds are a girl's best friend.

A
There

kiss may be grand but it won't pay the ren - tal on your
may come a time when a hard - boiled em - ploy - er thinks you're

hum - ble flat, or help you at the Au - to - mat.
aw - ful nice, but get that "ice" or else no dice.

Men grow cold as girls grow old, and we
He's your guy when stocks are high, but be -

all lose our charms in the end. But
- ware when they start to de - scend. It's

Drinking Song
(from 'The Student Prince')

Words & Music by Sigmund Romberg & Dorothy Donnelly

soon in - to mine! May those
soon a - round mine! May she

lips that are red and sweet to -
give me a price - less boon: a

- night with joy my own lips meet!
love be - neath the sweet, pale moon!

Drink! Drink! Let the toast start!

Empty Chairs At Empty Tables

(from 'Les Misérables')

Music by Claude-Michel Schönberg
Lyrics by Alain Boublil & Herbert Kretzmer

I'd Do Anything

(from 'Oliver!')

Words & Music by Lionel Bart

If I Were A Bell

(from 'Guys And Dolls')

Words & Music by Frank Loesser

* Symbols for Guitar, Diagrams for Ukulele.

If My Friends Could See Me Now

(from 'Sweet Charity')

Words by Dorothy Fields
Music by Cy Coleman

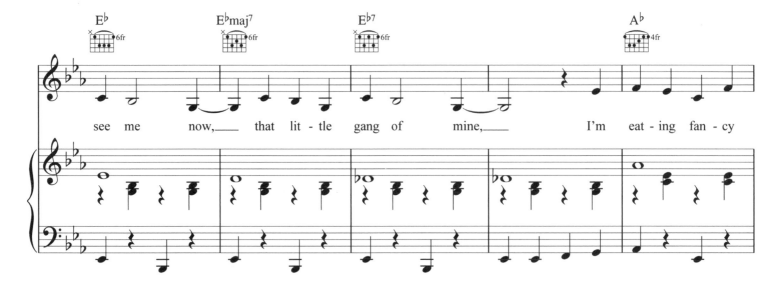

Knowing Me, Knowing You

(from 'Mamma Mia!')

Words & Music by Benny Andersson, Bjorn Ulvaeus & Stig Anderson

D.% al Coda

CODA

Know-ing me,   know-ing

do.

repeat and fade

The Ladies Who Lunch

(from 'Company')

Words & Music by Stephen Sondheim

78

The Last Night Of The World

(from 'Miss Saigon')

Music by Claude-Michel Schönberg
Lyrics by Alain Boublil & Richard Maltby Jr.
Adapted from original French Lyrics by Alain Boublil

Chris

In a place that won't let us feel.___

In a place where no-thing seems real.___ I have found you.___

83

84

hold me tight___ and dance, like it's the last night of the

world.___

Masquerade
(from 'The Phantom Of The Opera')

Music by Andrew Lloyd Webber
Lyrics by Charles Hart
Additional Lyrics by Richard Stilgoe

Mas-quer-ade,_____ pa-per fa-ces on pa-rade. Mas-quer-ade,_____ hide your face so the

world will nev - er find you. Mas-quer-ade,_____ ev-ery face a diff-erent shade,

mas - quer - ade,_____ look a-round there's an - oth - er mask be-hind you. Flash of

mauve, splash of puce, fool and king, ghoul and goose, green and black, queen and priest, trace of rouge, face of beast.

Fa - ces, take your turn, take a ride on the mer - ry-go round
In an in-hu - man Eye of

92

night, what a crowd, makes you glad, makes you proud, all the

crème de la crème, watch-ing us, watch-ing them, And all our fears are in the

three___ months of re-lief, of de-light, of El-y - si-an peace. No more
past.   And we can breathe at

notes, no more ghost, here's a health, here's a toast to a pros-per-ous year, to our friends who are here.
last.   And may our

Mr. Mistoffelees

(from 'Cats')

Music by Andrew Lloyd Webber
Text by T.S. Eliot

99

find it next week____ ly - ing out on the lawn.____
-duced se - ven kit - tens right out of a hat!____

To Coda ⊕
D.S. al Coda

And we all say:
And we all said:

f

⊕ *Coda* **Chorus**

F   C/E

oh! Well I nev - er! Was__ there

Gm⁷   C⁷   F   F/A   B♭

ev - er a cat so clev - er as Ma - gi - cal Mis - ter Mis - tof -

1.   *Repeat ad lib. 6 times* *Last time*

B♭/C   Dm

- fel - ees?   - fel - ees?

101

My Favourite Things

(from 'The Sound Of Music')

Words by Oscar Hammerstein II
Music by Richard Rodgers

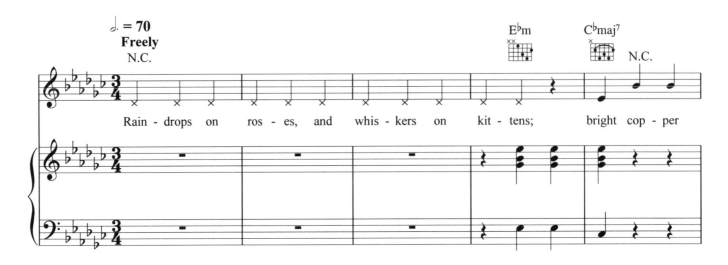

Rain - drops on ros - es, and whis - kers on kit - tens; bright cop - per

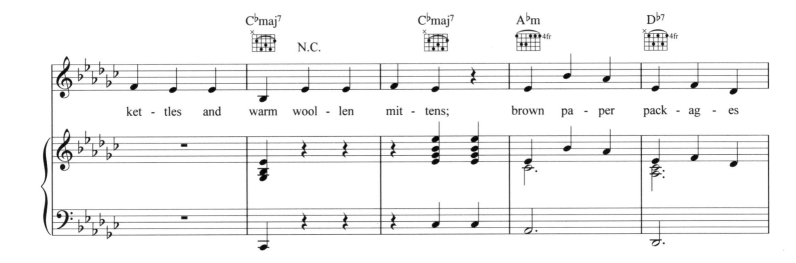

ket - tles and warm wool - len mit - tens; brown pa - per pack - ag - es

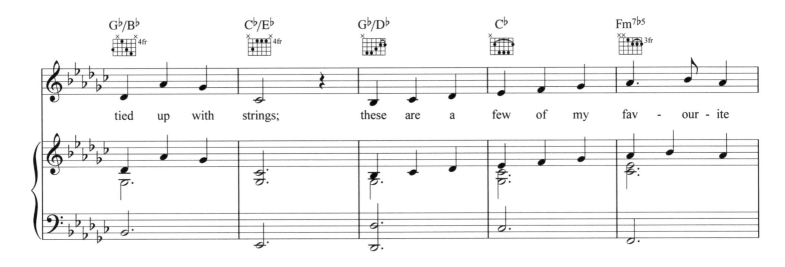

tied up with strings; these are a few of my fav - our - ite

When the dog bites, when the bee stings, when I'm feel - ing

sad,_____ I sim - ply re - mem - ber my fav - our - ite

things, and then I don't feel_____ so

bad._____

Once In Love With Amy

(from 'Where's Charley?')

Words & Music by Frank Loesser

1. I caught you,__ sir, hav-ing a look at__ her__ as
(2.) warn you,__ sir, nev-er to dream of__ her,__ just

she went__ stroll-ing by.___ Now, did -n't your heart go
bid such__ thoughts be - gone!___ Or it -'ll be boom boom

Rose-Tint My World

(from 'The Rocky Horror Show')

Words & Music by Chris O'Brien

117

-bi-do has-n't been con-trolled._____ Now the on-ly thing I've come to____ trust

____ is an or-gas-mic rush____ of lust:____

rose - tints my world, keeps me safe from my trou-ble and pain.____

It's be -

Sandy

(from 'Grease')

Words & Music by Louis St. Louis & Scott Simon

125

Shoes Upon The Table

(from 'Blood Brothers')

Words & Music by Willy Russell

Sunrise, Sunset

(from 'Fiddler On The Roof')

Words by Sheldon Harnick
Music by Jerry Bock

Verse 2:
Now is the little boy a bridegroom
Now is the little girl a bride
Under the canopy I see them side by side.
Place the gold ring around her finger
Share the sweet wine and break the glass
Soon the full circle will have come to pass.

Superstar
(from 'Jesus Christ Superstar')

Music by Andrew Lloyd Webber
Words by Tim Rice

1. Ev-'ry-time I look at you I don't un-der-stand, why you let the things you did get
2. Tell me what you think a-bout your friends at the top,— who d'you think be-sides your-self's the

so out of hand.— You'd have man-aged bet-ter if you'd had— it planned.—
pick of he crop?— Bud-dah was he where it's at? Is he where you are?——

136

Thank You Very Much

(from 'Scrooge')

Words & Music by Leslie Bricusse

therefore I would simply like to say:

1. Thank-you ve-ry much,
2. Thank-you ve-ry much,
(Verses 3 & 4 see block lyrics)

thank-you ve-ry much; that's the nic-est thing that a-ny-one's ev-er
thank-you ve-ry much; that's the nic-est thing that a-ny-one's ev-er

done for me. I may sound Dou-ble Dutch; but
done for me. It sounds a bit biz-are but,

Verse 3:
Thank you very much!
Thank you very much!
That's the nicest thing that anyone's ever done for me
It isn't everyday
Good fortune comes my way
I never thought the future would be fun for me
And if I had a bugle I would blow it
To add a sort of 'ow's-your-father touch
But since I left my bugle at home
I'll simply have to say
Thank you very, very, very much
Thank you very, very, very much.

Verse 4:
Thank you very much!
Thank you very much!
That's the nicest thing that anyone's ever done for me
The future looks all right
In fact it looks so bright
I'm thinking that they've been polishing the sun for me
And if I had a drum I'd have to bang it
To add a sort of rumpty-tumpty touch
But since I left my drum at home
I'll simply have to say
Thank you very, very, very much
Thank you very, very, very much.

When Will Someone Hear?

(from 'Martin Guerre')

Lyrics by Alain Boublil & Stephen Clark
Music by Claude-Michel Schönberg

When will some-one hear? Love that once was close,— faith that once was clear.—

Now all I've known and all I've loved is all I have to grieve.—

All that I've be-gun, all that I be-lieve is just a-no-ther bro-ken dream.—

When will some-one hear? They seem so strong,

With One Look

(from 'Sunset Boulevard')

Music by Andrew Lloyd Webber
Words by Don Black & Christopher Hampton

151

Younger Than Springtime

(from 'South Pacific')

Words by Oscar Hammerstein II
Music by Richard Rodgers

CHORUS (slowly with great warmth)

Tell Me On A Sunday

(from 'Tell Me On A Sunday')

Music by Andrew Lloyd Webber
Words by Don Black